S0-BSL-189

REDHEADS

MUSEUM OF FINE ARTS, BOSTON

Published in 1992 by
Museum of Fine Arts, Boston
Department of Retail Publications
295 Huntington Avenue
Boston, Massachusetts 02115

© MUSEUM OF FINE ARTS, BOSTON, 1992
All rights reserved, including the right to reproduce
this work in any form or by any means, electronic
or mechanical, including photocopy and
information retrieval systems, without permission
in writing from the Museum of Fine Arts, Boston.

ISBN 0-87846-352-6

COVER ILLUSTRATION:
Bocca Baciata (Lips That Have Been Kissed)
by Gabriel Charles Dante Rossetti
(British, 1828-1882)
Oil on panel, $12\frac{5}{8}$ x $10\frac{5}{8}$ inches
Gift of James Lawrence
1980.261

Design by Christopher Frame
Project Coordinator: Kathryn Sky-Peck

Printed and Bound in China

10 9 8 7 6 5

A

Lilian Westcott Hale
(American, 1881-1963)
L'Edition de Luxe , 1910 (detail)
Oil on canvas, 23¼ x 15 inches
Gift of Miss Mary C. Wheelwright
35.1487

NAME
_____

ADDRESS
_____
_____

TELEPHONE
_____

FACSIMILE
_____
_____

NAME
_____

ADDRESS
_____
_____

TELEPHONE
_____

FACSIMILE
_____
_____

NAME
_____

ADDRESS
_____
_____

TELEPHONE
_____

FACSIMILE
_____
_____

A

NAME

ADDRESS

TELEPHONE

FACSIMILE

NAME

ADDRESS

TELEPHONE

FACSIMILE

NAME

ADDRESS

TELEPHONE

FACSIMILE

NAME

ADDRESS

TELEPHONE

FACSIMILE

NAME

ADDRESS

TELEPHONE

FACSIMILE

NAME

ADDRESS

TELEPHONE

FACSIMILE

A

NAME

ADDRESS

TELEPHONE

FACSIMILE

NAME

ADDRESS

TELEPHONE

FACSIMILE

NAME

ADDRESS

TELEPHONE

FACSIMILE

A

NAME

ADDRESS

TELEPHONE

FACSIMILE

NAME

ADDRESS

TELEPHONE

FACSIMILE

NAME

ADDRESS

TELEPHONE

FACSIMILE

NAME

ADDRESS

TELEPHONE

FACSIMILE

NAME

ADDRESS

TELEPHONE

FACSIMILE

NAME

ADDRESS

TELEPHONE

FACSIMILE

A

NAME

ADDRESS

TELEPHONE

FACSIMILE

NAME

ADDRESS

TELEPHONE

FACSIMILE

NAME

ADDRESS

TELEPHONE

FACSIMILE

NAME

ADDRESS

TELEPHONE

FACSIMILE

NAME

ADDRESS

TELEPHONE

FACSIMILE

NAME

ADDRESS

TELEPHONE

FACSIMILE

NAME _____

ADDRESS _____

_____

TELEPHONE _____

FACSIMILE _____

_____

NAME _____

ADDRESS _____

_____

TELEPHONE _____

FACSIMILE _____

_____

NAME _____

ADDRESS _____

_____

TELEPHONE _____

FACSIMILE _____

_____

NAME _____

ADDRESS _____

_____

TELEPHONE _____

FACSIMILE _____

_____

NAME _____

ADDRESS _____

_____

TELEPHONE _____

FACSIMILE _____

_____

NAME _____

ADDRESS _____

_____

TELEPHONE _____

FACSIMILE _____

_____

A

NAME

ADDRESS

TELEPHONE

FACSIMILE

NAME

ADDRESS

TELEPHONE

FACSIMILE

NAME

ADDRESS

TELEPHONE

FACSIMILE

NAME

ADDRESS

TELEPHONE

FACSIMILE

NAME

ADDRESS

TELEPHONE

FACSIMILE

NAME

ADDRESS

TELEPHONE

FACSIMILE

B

B

Jefferson Gauntt
(American, 1806-1864)
Two Children, 1843
Oil on canvas, 50 x 40 inches
M. and M. Karolik Collection of
American Paintings
47.1161

NAME

ADDRESS

TELEPHONE

FACSIMILE

NAME

ADDRESS

TELEPHONE

FACSIMILE

NAME

ADDRESS

TELEPHONE

FACSIMILE

NAME	NAME
ADDRESS	ADDRESS
TELEPHONE	TELEPHONE
FACSIMILE	FACSIMILE

NAME	NAME
ADDRESS	ADDRESS
TELEPHONE	TELEPHONE
FACSIMILE	FACSIMILE

NAME	NAME
ADDRESS	ADDRESS
TELEPHONE	TELEPHONE
FACSIMILE	FACSIMILE

B

NAME

ADDRESS

TELEPHONE

FACSIMILE

NAME

ADDRESS

TELEPHONE

FACSIMILE

NAME

ADDRESS

TELEPHONE

FACSIMILE

NAME _____

ADDRESS _____

_____

TELEPHONE _____

FACSIMILE _____

_____

NAME _____

ADDRESS _____

_____

TELEPHONE _____

FACSIMILE _____

_____

NAME _____

ADDRESS _____

_____

TELEPHONE _____

FACSIMILE _____

_____

NAME _____

ADDRESS _____

_____

TELEPHONE _____

FACSIMILE _____

_____

NAME _____

ADDRESS _____

_____

TELEPHONE _____

FACSIMILE _____

_____

NAME _____

ADDRESS _____

_____

TELEPHONE _____

FACSIMILE _____

_____

NAME

ADDRESS

TELEPHONE

FACSIMILE

NAME

ADDRESS

TELEPHONE

FACSIMILE

NAME

ADDRESS

TELEPHONE

FACSIMILE

NAME

ADDRESS

TELEPHONE

FACSIMILE

NAME

ADDRESS

TELEPHONE

FACSIMILE

NAME

ADDRESS

TELEPHONE

FACSIMILE

NAME

ADDRESS

TELEPHONE

FACSIMILE

NAME

ADDRESS

TELEPHONE

FACSIMILE

NAME

ADDRESS

TELEPHONE

FACSIMILE

NAME

ADDRESS

TELEPHONE

FACSIMILE

NAME

ADDRESS

TELEPHONE

FACSIMILE

NAME

ADDRESS

TELEPHONE

FACSIMILE

B

NAME

ADDRESS

TELEPHONE

FACSIMILE

NAME

ADDRESS

TELEPHONE

FACSIMILE

NAME

ADDRESS

TELEPHONE

FACSIMILE

NAME

ADDRESS

TELEPHONE

FACSIMILE

NAME

ADDRESS

TELEPHONE

FACSIMILE

NAME

ADDRESS

TELEPHONE

FACSIMILE

C

Laura Coombs Hills
(American 1859-1952)
The Pink Flower (Viola Nilson), 1919
Watercolor on oval ivory, 4¾ x 4½ inches
Gift of Laura Coombs Hills

51.1937

NAME

ADDRESS

TELEPHONE

FACSIMILE

NAME

ADDRESS

TELEPHONE

FACSIMILE

NAME

ADDRESS

TELEPHONE

FACSIMILE

NAME

ADDRESS

TELEPHONE

FACSIMILE

NAME

ADDRESS

TELEPHONE

FACSIMILE

NAME

ADDRESS

TELEPHONE

FACSIMILE

NAME

ADDRESS

TELEPHONE

FACSIMILE

NAME

ADDRESS

TELEPHONE

FACSIMILE

NAME

ADDRESS

TELEPHONE

FACSIMILE

C

NAME

ADDRESS

TELEPHONE

FACSIMILE

NAME

ADDRESS

TELEPHONE

FACSIMILE

NAME

ADDRESS

TELEPHONE

FACSIMILE

NAME

ADDRESS

TELEPHONE

FACSIMILE

NAME

ADDRESS

TELEPHONE

FACSIMILE

NAME

ADDRESS

TELEPHONE

FACSIMILE

NAME

ADDRESS

TELEPHONE

FACSIMILE

NAME

ADDRESS

TELEPHONE

FACSIMILE

NAME

ADDRESS

TELEPHONE

FACSIMILE

NAME

ADDRESS

TELEPHONE

FACSIMILE

NAME

ADDRESS

TELEPHONE

FACSIMILE

NAME

ADDRESS

TELEPHONE

FACSIMILE

C

NAME

ADDRESS

TELEPHONE

FACSIMILE

NAME

ADDRESS

TELEPHONE

FACSIMILE

NAME

ADDRESS

TELEPHONE

FACSIMILE

NAME

ADDRESS

TELEPHONE

FACSIMILE

NAME

ADDRESS

TELEPHONE

FACSIMILE

NAME

ADDRESS

TELEPHONE

FACSIMILE

NAME

ADDRESS

TELEPHONE

FACSIMILE

NAME

ADDRESS

TELEPHONE

FACSIMILE

NAME

ADDRESS

TELEPHONE

FACSIMILE

NAME

ADDRESS

TELEPHONE

FACSIMILE

NAME

ADDRESS

TELEPHONE

FACSIMILE

NAME

ADDRESS

TELEPHONE

FACSIMILE

C

NAME

ADDRESS

TELEPHONE

FACSIMILE

NAME

ADDRESS

TELEPHONE

FACSIMILE

NAME

ADDRESS

TELEPHONE

FACSIMILE

NAME

ADDRESS

TELEPHONE

FACSIMILE

NAME

ADDRESS

TELEPHONE

FACSIMILE

NAME

ADDRESS

TELEPHONE

FACSIMILE

D

Edward Burne-Jones
(British, 1833-1898)
Hope, 1896 (detail)
Oil on canvas, 70 1/2 x 25 inches
Given in Memory of Mrs. George Marston
Whiting by her four daughters, Mrs. Laurence
Murray Keeler, Mrs. Sydney Russell Mason, Mrs.
Elijah Kent Swift and Mrs. William Carey Crane
40.778

NAME

ADDRESS

TELEPHONE

FACSIMILE

NAME

ADDRESS

TELEPHONE

FACSIMILE

NAME

ADDRESS

TELEPHONE

FACSIMILE

NAME

ADDRESS

TELEPHONE

FACSIMILE

NAME

ADDRESS

TELEPHONE

FACSIMILE

NAME

ADDRESS

TELEPHONE

FACSIMILE

NAME

ADDRESS

TELEPHONE

FACSIMILE

NAME

ADDRESS

TELEPHONE

FACSIMILE

NAME

ADDRESS

TELEPHONE

FACSIMILE

NAME

ADDRESS

TELEPHONE

FACSIMILE

NAME

ADDRESS

TELEPHONE

FACSIMILE

NAME

ADDRESS

TELEPHONE

FACSIMILE

NAME

ADDRESS

TELEPHONE

FACSIMILE

NAME

ADDRESS

TELEPHONE

FACSIMILE

NAME

ADDRESS

TELEPHONE

FACSIMILE

NAME

ADDRESS

TELEPHONE

FACSIMILE

NAME

ADDRESS

TELEPHONE

FACSIMILE

NAME

ADDRESS

TELEPHONE

FACSIMILE

D

NAME	NAME
ADDRESS	ADDRESS
TELEPHONE	TELEPHONE
FACSIMILE	FACSIMILE
NAME	NAME
ADDRESS	ADDRESS
TELEPHONE	TELEPHONE
FACSIMILE	FACSIMILE
NAME	NAME
ADDRESS	ADDRESS
TELEPHONE	TELEPHONE
FACSIMILE	FACSIMILE

D

NAME

ADDRESS

TELEPHONE

FACSIMILE

NAME

ADDRESS

TELEPHONE

FACSIMILE

NAME

ADDRESS

TELEPHONE

FACSIMILE

NAME

ADDRESS

TELEPHONE

FACSIMILE

NAME

ADDRESS

TELEPHONE

FACSIMILE

NAME

ADDRESS

TELEPHONE

FACSIMILE

NAME

ADDRESS

TELEPHONE

FACSIMILE

NAME

ADDRESS

TELEPHONE

FACSIMILE

NAME

ADDRESS

TELEPHONE

FACSIMILE

NAME

ADDRESS

TELEPHONE

FACSIMILE

NAME

ADDRESS

TELEPHONE

FACSIMILE

NAME

ADDRESS

TELEPHONE

FACSIMILE

E

Gabriel Charles Dante Rossetti
(British, 1828-1882)
Bocca Baciata (Lips That Have Been Kissed)
Oil on panel, $12\frac{5}{8}$ x $10\frac{5}{8}$ inches
Gift of James Lawrence
1980.261

NAME

ADDRESS

TELEPHONE

FACSIMILE

NAME

ADDRESS

TELEPHONE

FACSIMILE

NAME

ADDRESS

TELEPHONE

FACSIMILE

NAME

ADDRESS

TELEPHONE

FACSIMILE

NAME

ADDRESS

TELEPHONE

FACSIMILE

NAME

ADDRESS

TELEPHONE

FACSIMILE

NAME

ADDRESS

TELEPHONE

FACSIMILE

NAME

ADDRESS

TELEPHONE

FACSIMILE

NAME

ADDRESS

TELEPHONE

FACSIMILE

E

NAME

ADDRESS

TELEPHONE

FACSIMILE

NAME

ADDRESS

TELEPHONE

FACSIMILE

NAME

ADDRESS

TELEPHONE

FACSIMILE

NAME

ADDRESS

TELEPHONE

FACSIMILE

NAME

ADDRESS

TELEPHONE

FACSIMILE

NAME

ADDRESS

TELEPHONE

FACSIMILE

NAME

ADDRESS

TELEPHONE

FACSIMILE

NAME

ADDRESS

TELEPHONE

FACSIMILE

NAME

ADDRESS

TELEPHONE

FACSIMILE

NAME

ADDRESS

TELEPHONE

FACSIMILE

NAME

ADDRESS

TELEPHONE

FACSIMILE

NAME

ADDRESS

TELEPHONE

FACSIMILE

NAME

ADDRESS

TELEPHONE

FACSIMILE

NAME

ADDRESS

TELEPHONE

FACSIMILE

NAME

ADDRESS

TELEPHONE

FACSIMILE

NAME

ADDRESS

TELEPHONE

FACSIMILE

NAME

ADDRESS

TELEPHONE

FACSIMILE

NAME

ADDRESS

TELEPHONE

FACSIMILE

NAME

ADDRESS

TELEPHONE

FACSIMILE

NAME

ADDRESS

TELEPHONE

FACSIMILE

NAME

ADDRESS

TELEPHONE

FACSIMILE

NAME

ADDRESS

TELEPHONE

FACSIMILE

E

NAME

ADDRESS

TELEPHONE

FACSIMILE

NAME

ADDRESS

TELEPHONE

FACSIMILE

NAME

ADDRESS

TELEPHONE

FACSIMILE

NAME

ADDRESS

TELEPHONE

FACSIMILE

NAME

ADDRESS

TELEPHONE

FACSIMILE

NAME

ADDRESS

TELEPHONE

FACSIMILE

F

Lorenzo Costa
(Italian [Ferrare], about 1460-1535)
Portrait of a Woman with a Pearl Necklace
Oil on panel, 17 3/8 x 13 3/8 inches
Bequest of Mrs. Thomas O. Richardson
25.227

NAME

ADDRESS

TELEPHONE

FACSIMILE

NAME

ADDRESS

TELEPHONE

FACSIMILE

NAME

ADDRESS

TELEPHONE

FACSIMILE

F

NAME

ADDRESS

TELEPHONE

FACSIMILE

NAME

ADDRESS

TELEPHONE

FACSIMILE

NAME

ADDRESS

TELEPHONE

FACSIMILE

NAME

ADDRESS

TELEPHONE

FACSIMILE

NAME

ADDRESS

TELEPHONE

FACSIMILE

NAME

ADDRESS

TELEPHONE

FACSIMILE

F

NAME

ADDRESS

TELEPHONE

FACSIMILE

NAME

ADDRESS

TELEPHONE

FACSIMILE

NAME

ADDRESS

TELEPHONE

FACSIMILE

NAME

ADDRESS

TELEPHONE

FACSIMILE

NAME

ADDRESS

TELEPHONE

FACSIMILE

NAME

ADDRESS

TELEPHONE

FACSIMILE

NAME

ADDRESS

TELEPHONE

FACSIMILE

NAME

ADDRESS

TELEPHONE

FACSIMILE

NAME

ADDRESS

TELEPHONE

FACSIMILE

NAME

ADDRESS

TELEPHONE

FACSIMILE

NAME

ADDRESS

TELEPHONE

FACSIMILE

NAME

ADDRESS

TELEPHONE

FACSIMILE

NAME

ADDRESS

TELEPHONE

FACSIMILE

NAME

ADDRESS

TELEPHONE

FACSIMILE

NAME

ADDRESS

TELEPHONE

FACSIMILE

NAME

ADDRESS

TELEPHONE

FACSIMILE

NAME

ADDRESS

TELEPHONE

FACSIMILE

NAME

ADDRESS

TELEPHONE

FACSIMILE

F

NAME

ADDRESS

TELEPHONE

FACSIMILE

NAME

ADDRESS

TELEPHONE

FACSIMILE

NAME

ADDRESS

TELEPHONE

FACSIMILE

NAME

ADDRESS

TELEPHONE

FACSIMILE

NAME

ADDRESS

TELEPHONE

FACSIMILE

NAME

ADDRESS

TELEPHONE

FACSIMILE

F

NAME

ADDRESS

TELEPHONE

FACSIMILE

NAME

ADDRESS

TELEPHONE

FACSIMILE

NAME

ADDRESS

TELEPHONE

FACSIMILE

NAME

ADDRESS

TELEPHONE

FACSIMILE

NAME

ADDRESS

TELEPHONE

FACSIMILE

NAME

ADDRESS

TELEPHONE

FACSIMILE

Edward Coley Burne-Jones
(British, 1833-1898)
Le Chant D'Amour (The Song of Love), 1865
Gouache on paper, 22 x 30 ¾ inches
Bequest of Martin Brimmer
06. 2432

NAME

ADDRESS

TELEPHONE

FACSIMILE

NAME

ADDRESS

TELEPHONE

FACSIMILE

NAME

ADDRESS

TELEPHONE

FACSIMILE

NAME

ADDRESS

TELEPHONE

FACSIMILE

NAME

ADDRESS

TELEPHONE

FACSIMILE

NAME

ADDRESS

TELEPHONE

FACSIMILE

NAME

ADDRESS

TELEPHONE

FACSIMILE

NAME

ADDRESS

TELEPHONE

FACSIMILE

NAME

ADDRESS

TELEPHONE

FACSIMILE

NAME

ADDRESS

TELEPHONE

FACSIMILE

NAME

ADDRESS

TELEPHONE

FACSIMILE

NAME

ADDRESS

TELEPHONE

FACSIMILE

NAME

ADDRESS

TELEPHONE

FACSIMILE

NAME

ADDRESS

TELEPHONE

FACSIMILE

NAME

ADDRESS

TELEPHONE

FACSIMILE

G

NAME

ADDRESS

TELEPHONE

FACSIMILE

NAME

ADDRESS

TELEPHONE

FACSIMILE

NAME

ADDRESS

TELEPHONE

FACSIMILE

NAME

ADDRESS

TELEPHONE

FACSIMILE

NAME

ADDRESS

TELEPHONE

FACSIMILE

NAME

ADDRESS

TELEPHONE

FACSIMILE

NAME

ADDRESS

TELEPHONE

FACSIMILE

NAME

ADDRESS

TELEPHONE

FACSIMILE

NAME

ADDRESS

TELEPHONE

FACSIMILE

NAME

ADDRESS

TELEPHONE

FACSIMILE

NAME

ADDRESS

TELEPHONE

FACSIMILE

NAME

ADDRESS

TELEPHONE

FACSIMILE

NAME

ADDRESS

TELEPHONE

FACSIMILE

NAME

ADDRESS

TELEPHONE

FACSIMILE

NAME

ADDRESS

TELEPHONE

FACSIMILE

G

NAME

ADDRESS

TELEPHONE

FACSIMILE

NAME

ADDRESS

TELEPHONE

FACSIMILE

NAME

ADDRESS

TELEPHONE

FACSIMILE

NAME

ADDRESS

TELEPHONE

FACSIMILE

NAME

ADDRESS

TELEPHONE

FACSIMILE

NAME

ADDRESS

TELEPHONE

FACSIMILE

H

Hilaire Germaine Edgar Degas
(French, 1834-1917)
Dancers in Rose
Pastel on paper, 33⅛ x 22⅞ inches
Seth K. Sweetser Fund
20. 164

NAME

ADDRESS

TELEPHONE

FACSIMILE

NAME

ADDRESS

TELEPHONE

FACSIMILE

NAME

ADDRESS

TELEPHONE

FACSIMILE

NAME

ADDRESS

TELEPHONE

FACSIMILE

NAME

ADDRESS

TELEPHONE

FACSIMILE

NAME

ADDRESS

TELEPHONE

FACSIMILE

NAME

ADDRESS

TELEPHONE

FACSIMILE

NAME

ADDRESS

TELEPHONE

FACSIMILE

NAME

ADDRESS

TELEPHONE

FACSIMILE

NAME

ADDRESS

TELEPHONE

FACSIMILE

NAME

ADDRESS

TELEPHONE

FACSIMILE

NAME

ADDRESS

TELEPHONE

FACSIMILE

NAME

ADDRESS

TELEPHONE

FACSIMILE

NAME

ADDRESS

TELEPHONE

FACSIMILE

NAME

ADDRESS

TELEPHONE

FACSIMILE

NAME

ADDRESS

TELEPHONE

FACSIMILE

NAME

ADDRESS

TELEPHONE

FACSIMILE

NAME

ADDRESS

TELEPHONE

FACSIMILE

NAME

ADDRESS

TELEPHONE

FACSIMILE

NAME

ADDRESS

TELEPHONE

FACSIMILE

NAME

ADDRESS

TELEPHONE

FACSIMILE

NAME

ADDRESS

TELEPHONE

FACSIMILE

NAME

ADDRESS

TELEPHONE

FACSIMILE

NAME

ADDRESS

TELEPHONE

FACSIMILE

NAME

ADDRESS

TELEPHONE

FACSIMILE

NAME

ADDRESS

TELEPHONE

FACSIMILE

NAME

ADDRESS

TELEPHONE

FACSIMILE

NAME

ADDRESS

TELEPHONE

FACSIMILE

NAME

ADDRESS

TELEPHONE

FACSIMILE

NAME

ADDRESS

TELEPHONE

FACSIMILE

NAME

ADDRESS

TELEPHONE

FACSIMILE

NAME

ADDRESS

TELEPHONE

FACSIMILE

NAME

ADDRESS

TELEPHONE

FACSIMILE

H

NAME

ADDRESS

TELEPHONE

FACSIMILE

NAME

ADDRESS

TELEPHONE

FACSIMILE

NAME

ADDRESS

TELEPHONE

FACSIMILE

NAME

ADDRESS

TELEPHONE

FACSIMILE

NAME

ADDRESS

TELEPHONE

FACSIMILE

NAME

ADDRESS

TELEPHONE

FACSIMILE

Laura Coombs Hills

(American 1859-1952)

Bertha Coolidge, 1911

Watercolor on oval ivory, 6 x 4¼ inches

Gift of Laura Coombs Hills

51.1931

NAME

ADDRESS

TELEPHONE

FACSIMILE

NAME

ADDRESS

TELEPHONE

FACSIMILE

NAME

ADDRESS

TELEPHONE

FACSIMILE

NAME

ADDRESS

TELEPHONE

FACSIMILE

NAME

ADDRESS

TELEPHONE

FACSIMILE

NAME

ADDRESS

TELEPHONE

FACSIMILE

NAME

ADDRESS

TELEPHONE

FACSIMILE

NAME

ADDRESS

TELEPHONE

FACSIMILE

NAME

ADDRESS

TELEPHONE

FACSIMILE

I

NAME

ADDRESS

TELEPHONE

FACSIMILE

NAME

ADDRESS

TELEPHONE

FACSIMILE

NAME

ADDRESS

TELEPHONE

FACSIMILE

NAME

ADDRESS

TELEPHONE

FACSIMILE

I

NAME

ADDRESS

TELEPHONE

FACSIMILE

NAME

ADDRESS

TELEPHONE

FACSIMILE

NAME

ADDRESS

TELEPHONE

FACSIMILE

NAME

ADDRESS

TELEPHONE

FACSIMILE

NAME

ADDRESS

TELEPHONE

FACSIMILE

NAME

ADDRESS

TELEPHONE

FACSIMILE

I

NAME

ADDRESS

TELEPHONE

FACSIMILE

NAME

ADDRESS

TELEPHONE

FACSIMILE

NAME

ADDRESS

TELEPHONE

FACSIMILE

NAME

ADDRESS

TELEPHONE

FACSIMILE

NAME

ADDRESS

TELEPHONE

FACSIMILE

NAME

ADDRESS

TELEPHONE

FACSIMILE

NAME

ADDRESS

TELEPHONE

FACSIMILE

NAME

ADDRESS

TELEPHONE

FACSIMILE

NAME

ADDRESS

TELEPHONE

FACSIMILE

NAME

ADDRESS

TELEPHONE

FACSIMILE

NAME

ADDRESS

TELEPHONE

FACSIMILE

NAME

ADDRESS

TELEPHONE

FACSIMILE

I

NAME

ADDRESS

TELEPHONE

FACSIMILE

NAME

ADDRESS

TELEPHONE

FACSIMILE

NAME

ADDRESS

TELEPHONE

FACSIMILE

NAME

ADDRESS

TELEPHONE

FACSIMILE

NAME

ADDRESS

TELEPHONE

FACSIMILE

NAME

ADDRESS

TELEPHONE

FACSIMILE

Pierre Auguste Renoir
(French, 1841-1919)
Jacques Bergeret as a Child
Oil on canvas, 16⅛ x 12¾ inches
Bequest of John T. Spaulding
48.595

NAME

ADDRESS

TELEPHONE

FACSIMILE

NAME

ADDRESS

TELEPHONE

FACSIMILE

NAME

ADDRESS

TELEPHONE

FACSIMILE

NAME

ADDRESS

TELEPHONE

FACSIMILE

NAME

ADDRESS

TELEPHONE

FACSIMILE

NAME

ADDRESS

TELEPHONE

FACSIMILE

NAME

ADDRESS

TELEPHONE

FACSIMILE

NAME

ADDRESS

TELEPHONE

FACSIMILE

NAME

ADDRESS

TELEPHONE

FACSIMILE

J

NAME

ADDRESS

TELEPHONE

FACSIMILE

NAME

ADDRESS

TELEPHONE

FACSIMILE

NAME

ADDRESS

TELEPHONE

FACSIMILE

NAME

ADDRESS

TELEPHONE

FACSIMILE

NAME

ADDRESS

TELEPHONE

FACSIMILE

NAME

ADDRESS

TELEPHONE

FACSIMILE

NAME

ADDRESS

TELEPHONE

FACSIMILE

NAME

ADDRESS

TELEPHONE

FACSIMILE

NAME

ADDRESS

TELEPHONE

FACSIMILE

NAME

ADDRESS

TELEPHONE

FACSIMILE

NAME

ADDRESS

TELEPHONE

FACSIMILE

NAME

ADDRESS

TELEPHONE

FACSIMILE

J

NAME

ADDRESS

TELEPHONE

FACSIMILE

NAME

ADDRESS

TELEPHONE

FACSIMILE

NAME

ADDRESS

TELEPHONE

FACSIMILE

NAME

ADDRESS

TELEPHONE

FACSIMILE

NAME

ADDRESS

TELEPHONE

FACSIMILE

NAME

ADDRESS

TELEPHONE

FACSIMILE

NAME

ADDRESS

TELEPHONE

FACSIMILE

NAME

ADDRESS

TELEPHONE

FACSIMILE

NAME

ADDRESS

TELEPHONE

FACSIMILE

NAME

ADDRESS

TELEPHONE

FACSIMILE

NAME

ADDRESS

TELEPHONE

FACSIMILE

NAME

ADDRESS

TELEPHONE

FACSIMILE

J

NAME

ADDRESS

TELEPHONE

FACSIMILE

NAME

ADDRESS

TELEPHONE

FACSIMILE

NAME

ADDRESS

TELEPHONE

FACSIMILE

NAME

ADDRESS

TELEPHONE

FACSIMILE

NAME

ADDRESS

TELEPHONE

FACSIMILE

NAME

ADDRESS

TELEPHONE

FACSIMILE

Arthur Spear
(American, 1879-1959)
Ophelia
Oil on canvas, 26 x 32⅛ inches
Gift of Mr. and Mrs. Matt B. Jones, Jr.
1987.246

NAME

ADDRESS

TELEPHONE

FACSIMILE

NAME

ADDRESS

TELEPHONE

FACSIMILE

NAME

ADDRESS

TELEPHONE

FACSIMILE

NAME

ADDRESS

TELEPHONE

FACSIMILE

NAME

ADDRESS

TELEPHONE

FACSIMILE

NAME

ADDRESS

TELEPHONE

FACSIMILE

NAME

ADDRESS

TELEPHONE

FACSIMILE

NAME

ADDRESS

TELEPHONE

FACSIMILE

NAME

ADDRESS

TELEPHONE

FACSIMILE

K

NAME

ADDRESS

TELEPHONE

FACSIMILE

NAME

ADDRESS

TELEPHONE

FACSIMILE

NAME

ADDRESS

TELEPHONE

FACSIMILE

NAME

ADDRESS

TELEPHONE

FACSIMILE

NAME

ADDRESS

TELEPHONE

FACSIMILE

NAME

ADDRESS

TELEPHONE

FACSIMILE

NAME

ADDRESS

TELEPHONE

FACSIMILE

NAME

ADDRESS

TELEPHONE

FACSIMILE

NAME

ADDRESS

TELEPHONE

FACSIMILE

NAME

ADDRESS

TELEPHONE

FACSIMILE

NAME

ADDRESS

TELEPHONE

FACSIMILE

NAME

ADDRESS

TELEPHONE

FACSIMILE

NAME

ADDRESS

TELEPHONE

FACSIMILE

NAME

ADDRESS

TELEPHONE

FACSIMILE

NAME

ADDRESS

TELEPHONE

FACSIMILE

NAME

ADDRESS

TELEPHONE

FACSIMILE

NAME

ADDRESS

TELEPHONE

FACSIMILE

K

NAME

ADDRESS

TELEPHONE

FACSIMILE

NAME

ADDRESS

TELEPHONE

FACSIMILE

NAME

ADDRESS

TELEPHONE

FACSIMILE

NAME

ADDRESS

TELEPHONE

FACSIMILE

NAME

ADDRESS

TELEPHONE

FACSIMILE

NAME

ADDRESS

TELEPHONE

FACSIMILE

K

NAME

ADDRESS

TELEPHONE

FACSIMILE

NAME

ADDRESS

TELEPHONE

FACSIMILE

NAME

ADDRESS

TELEPHONE

FACSIMILE

NAME

ADDRESS

TELEPHONE

FACSIMILE

NAME

ADDRESS

TELEPHONE

FACSIMILE

NAME

ADDRESS

TELEPHONE

FACSIMILE

L

Vincent van Gogh
(Dutch [worked in France], 1853–1890)
*Lullaby: Madame Augustine Roulin Rocking
a Cradle (La Berceuse)*
Oil on canvas, 36½ x 28⅝ inches
Bequest of John T. Spaulding
48.548

NAME

ADDRESS

TELEPHONE

FACSIMILE

NAME

ADDRESS

TELEPHONE

FACSIMILE

NAME

ADDRESS

TELEPHONE

FACSIMILE

NAME

ADDRESS

TELEPHONE

FACSIMILE

NAME

ADDRESS

TELEPHONE

FACSIMILE

NAME

ADDRESS

TELEPHONE

FACSIMILE

NAME

ADDRESS

TELEPHONE

FACSIMILE

NAME

ADDRESS

TELEPHONE

FACSIMILE

NAME

ADDRESS

TELEPHONE

FACSIMILE

L

NAME

ADDRESS

TELEPHONE

FACSIMILE

NAME

ADDRESS

TELEPHONE

FACSIMILE

NAME

ADDRESS

TELEPHONE

FACSIMILE

NAME

ADDRESS

TELEPHONE

FACSIMILE

NAME

ADDRESS

TELEPHONE

FACSIMILE

NAME

ADDRESS

TELEPHONE

FACSIMILE

NAME

ADDRESS

TELEPHONE

FACSIMILE

NAME

ADDRESS

TELEPHONE

FACSIMILE

NAME

ADDRESS

TELEPHONE

FACSIMILE

NAME

ADDRESS

TELEPHONE

FACSIMILE

NAME

ADDRESS

TELEPHONE

FACSIMILE

NAME

ADDRESS

TELEPHONE

FACSIMILE

L

NAME

ADDRESS

TELEPHONE

FACSIMILE

NAME

ADDRESS

TELEPHONE

FACSIMILE

NAME

ADDRESS

TELEPHONE

FACSIMILE

NAME

ADDRESS

TELEPHONE

FACSIMILE

NAME

ADDRESS

TELEPHONE

FACSIMILE

NAME

ADDRESS

TELEPHONE

FACSIMILE

L

NAME

ADDRESS

TELEPHONE

FACSIMILE

NAME

ADDRESS

TELEPHONE

FACSIMILE

NAME

ADDRESS

TELEPHONE

FACSIMILE

NAME

ADDRESS

TELEPHONE

FACSIMILE

NAME

ADDRESS

TELEPHONE

FACSIMILE

NAME

ADDRESS

TELEPHONE

FACSIMILE

L

NAME

ADDRESS

TELEPHONE

FACSIMILE

NAME

ADDRESS

TELEPHONE

FACSIMILE

NAME

ADDRESS

TELEPHONE

FACSIMILE

NAME

ADDRESS

TELEPHONE

FACSIMILE

NAME

ADDRESS

TELEPHONE

FACSIMILE

NAME

ADDRESS

TELEPHONE

FACSIMILE

Hilaire Germain Edgar Degas
(French, 1834-1917)
Dancer, about 1878
Pastel on paper mounted on cardboard,
30 1/4 x 17 3/4 inches
Tompkins Collection
35.27

NAME

ADDRESS

TELEPHONE

FACSIMILE

NAME

ADDRESS

TELEPHONE

FACSIMILE

NAME

ADDRESS

TELEPHONE

FACSIMILE

NAME

ADDRESS

TELEPHONE

FACSIMILE

NAME

ADDRESS

TELEPHONE

FACSIMILE

NAME

ADDRESS

TELEPHONE

FACSIMILE

NAME

ADDRESS

TELEPHONE

FACSIMILE

NAME

ADDRESS

TELEPHONE

FACSIMILE

NAME

ADDRESS

TELEPHONE

FACSIMILE

NAME

ADDRESS

TELEPHONE

FACSIMILE

NAME

ADDRESS

TELEPHONE

FACSIMILE

NAME

ADDRESS

TELEPHONE

FACSIMILE

NAME

ADDRESS

TELEPHONE

FACSIMILE

NAME

ADDRESS

TELEPHONE

FACSIMILE

NAME

ADDRESS

TELEPHONE

FACSIMILE

NAME

ADDRESS

TELEPHONE

FACSIMILE

NAME

ADDRESS

TELEPHONE

FACSIMILE

NAME

ADDRESS

TELEPHONE

FACSIMILE

NAME

ADDRESS

TELEPHONE

FACSIMILE

NAME

ADDRESS

TELEPHONE

FACSIMILE

NAME

ADDRESS

TELEPHONE

FACSIMILE

NAME

ADDRESS

TELEPHONE

FACSIMILE

NAME

ADDRESS

TELEPHONE

FACSIMILE

NAME

ADDRESS

TELEPHONE

FACSIMILE

NAME

ADDRESS

TELEPHONE

FACSIMILE

NAME

ADDRESS

TELEPHONE

FACSIMILE

NAME

ADDRESS

TELEPHONE

FACSIMILE

NAME

ADDRESS

TELEPHONE

FACSIMILE

NAME

ADDRESS

TELEPHONE

FACSIMILE

NAME

ADDRESS

TELEPHONE

FACSIMILE

NAME

ADDRESS

TELEPHONE

FACSIMILE

NAME

ADDRESS

TELEPHONE

FACSIMILE

NAME

ADDRESS

TELEPHONE

FACSIMILE

NAME

ADDRESS

TELEPHONE

FACSIMILE

NAME

ADDRESS

TELEPHONE

FACSIMILE

NAME

ADDRESS

TELEPHONE

FACSIMILE

Dennis Miller Bunker
(American, 1861–1890)
Jessica, 1890
Oil on canvas, 26 x 24 inches
Gift by contribution ©
91.130

NAME

ADDRESS

TELEPHONE

FACSIMILE

NAME

ADDRESS

TELEPHONE

FACSIMILE

NAME

ADDRESS

TELEPHONE

FACSIMILE

NAME

ADDRESS

TELEPHONE

FACSIMILE

NAME

ADDRESS

TELEPHONE

FACSIMILE

NAME

ADDRESS

TELEPHONE

FACSIMILE

NAME

ADDRESS

TELEPHONE

FACSIMILE

NAME

ADDRESS

TELEPHONE

FACSIMILE

NAME

ADDRESS

TELEPHONE

FACSIMILE

NAME

ADDRESS

TELEPHONE

FACSIMILE

NAME

ADDRESS

TELEPHONE

FACSIMILE

NAME

ADDRESS

TELEPHONE

FACSIMILE

NAME

ADDRESS

TELEPHONE

FACSIMILE

NAME

ADDRESS

TELEPHONE

FACSIMILE

NAME

ADDRESS

TELEPHONE

FACSIMILE

NAME

ADDRESS

TELEPHONE

FACSIMILE

NAME

ADDRESS

TELEPHONE

FACSIMILE

NAME

ADDRESS

TELEPHONE

FACSIMILE

NAME

ADDRESS

TELEPHONE

FACSIMILE

NAME

ADDRESS

TELEPHONE

FACSIMILE

NAME

ADDRESS

TELEPHONE

FACSIMILE

NAME

ADDRESS

TELEPHONE

FACSIMILE

NAME

ADDRESS

TELEPHONE

FACSIMILE

NAME

ADDRESS

TELEPHONE

FACSIMILE

NAME

ADDRESS

TELEPHONE

FACSIMILE

NAME

ADDRESS

TELEPHONE

FACSIMILE

NAME

ADDRESS

TELEPHONE

FACSIMILE

NAME

ADDRESS

TELEPHONE

FACSIMILE

NAME

ADDRESS

TELEPHONE

FACSIMILE

NAME

ADDRESS

TELEPHONE

FACSIMILE

NAME

ADDRESS

TELEPHONE

FACSIMILE

NAME

ADDRESS

TELEPHONE

FACSIMILE

NAME

ADDRESS

TELEPHONE

FACSIMILE

NAME

ADDRESS

TELEPHONE

FACSIMILE

NAME

ADDRESS

TELEPHONE

FACSIMILE

NAME

ADDRESS

TELEPHONE

FACSIMILE

NAME

ADDRESS

TELEPHONE

FACSIMILE

NAME

ADDRESS

TELEPHONE

FACSIMILE

NAME

ADDRESS

TELEPHONE

FACSIMILE

Frank Weston Benson
(American, 1862-1951)
Eleanor, 1907 (detail)
Oil on canvas, 25 x 30 inches
The Hayden Collection
08.326

NAME

ADDRESS

TELEPHONE

FACSIMILE

NAME

ADDRESS

TELEPHONE

FACSIMILE

NAME

ADDRESS

TELEPHONE

FACSIMILE

NAME

ADDRESS

TELEPHONE

FACSIMILE

NAME

ADDRESS

TELEPHONE

FACSIMILE

NAME

ADDRESS

TELEPHONE

FACSIMILE

NAME

ADDRESS

TELEPHONE

FACSIMILE

NAME

ADDRESS

TELEPHONE

FACSIMILE

NAME

ADDRESS

TELEPHONE

FACSIMILE

NAME

ADDRESS

TELEPHONE

FACSIMILE

NAME

ADDRESS

TELEPHONE

FACSIMILE

NAME

ADDRESS

TELEPHONE

FACSIMILE

NAME

ADDRESS

TELEPHONE

FACSIMILE

NAME

ADDRESS

TELEPHONE

FACSIMILE

NAME

ADDRESS

TELEPHONE

FACSIMILE

O

NAME

ADDRESS

TELEPHONE

FACSIMILE

NAME

ADDRESS

TELEPHONE

FACSIMILE

NAME

ADDRESS

TELEPHONE

FACSIMILE

NAME

ADDRESS

TELEPHONE

FACSIMILE

NAME

ADDRESS

TELEPHONE

FACSIMILE

NAME

ADDRESS

TELEPHONE

FACSIMILE

NAME

ADDRESS

TELEPHONE

FACSIMILE

NAME

ADDRESS

TELEPHONE

FACSIMILE

NAME

ADDRESS

TELEPHONE

FACSIMILE

NAME

ADDRESS

TELEPHONE

FACSIMILE

NAME

ADDRESS

TELEPHONE

FACSIMILE

NAME

ADDRESS

TELEPHONE

FACSIMILE

NAME

ADDRESS

TELEPHONE

FACSIMILE

NAME

ADDRESS

TELERHONE

FACSIMILE

NAME

ADDRESS

TELEPHONE

FACSIMILE

NAME

ADDRESS

TELEPHONE

FACSIMILE

NAME

ADDRESS

TELEPHONE

FACSIMILE

NAME

ADDRESS

TELEPHONE

FACSIMILE

NAME

ADDRESS

TELEPHONE

FACSIMILE

NAME

ADDRESS

TELEPHONE

FACSIMILE

NAME

ADDRESS

TELEPHONE

FACSIMILE

NAME

ADDRESS

TELEPHONE

FACSIMILE

Mary Stevenson Cassatt
(American, 1844-1926)
Young Woman Reading
Oil on panel, 13¾ x 10½ inches
Bequest of John T. Spaulding
48.523

NAME

ADDRESS

TELEPHONE

FACSIMILE

NAME

ADDRESS

TELEPHONE

FACSIMILE

NAME

ADDRESS

TELEPHONE

FACSIMILE

NAME

ADDRESS

TELEPHONE

FACSIMILE

NAME

ADDRESS

TELEPHONE

FACSIMILE

NAME

ADDRESS

TELEPHONE

FACSIMILE

NAME

ADDRESS

TELEPHONE

FACSIMILE

NAME

ADDRESS

TELEPHONE

FACSIMILE

NAME

ADDRESS

TELEPHONE

FACSIMILE

NAME

ADDRESS

TELEPHONE

FACSIMILE

NAME

ADDRESS

TELEPHONE

FACSIMILE

NAME

ADDRESS

TELEPHONE

FACSIMILE

NAME

ADDRESS

TELEPHONE

FACSIMILE

NAME

ADDRESS

TELEPHONE

FACSIMILE

NAME

ADDRESS

TELEPHONE

FACSIMILE

NAME

ADDRESS

TELEPHONE

FACSIMILE

NAME

ADDRESS

TELEPHONE

FACSIMILE

NAME

ADDRESS

TELEPHONE

FACSIMILE

NAME

ADDRESS

TELEPHONE

FACSIMILE

P Q

NAME

ADDRESS

TELEPHONE

FACSIMILE

NAME

ADDRESS

TELEPHONE

FACSIMILE

NAME

ADDRESS

TELEPHONE

FACSIMILE

NAME

ADDRESS

TELEPHONE

FACSIMILE

NAME

ADDRESS

TELEPHONE

FACSIMILE

NAME

ADDRESS

TELEPHONE

FACSIMILE

NAME

ADDRESS

TELEPHONE

FACSIMILE

NAME

ADDRESS

TELEPHONE

FACSIMILE

NAME

ADDRESS

TELEPHONE

FACSIMILE

NAME

ADDRESS

TELEPHONE

FACSIMILE

NAME

ADDRESS

TELEPHONE

FACSIMILE

NAME

ADDRESS

TELEPHONE

FACSIMILE

P Q

NAME

ADDRESS

TELEPHONE

FACSIMILE

NAME

ADDRESS

TELEPHONE

FACSIMILE

NAME

ADDRESS

TELEPHONE

FACSIMILE

NAME

ADDRESS

TELEPHONE

FACSIMILE

NAME

ADDRESS

TELEPHONE

FACSIMILE

NAME

ADDRESS

TELEPHONE

FACSIMILE

Laura Coombs Hills
(American 1859-1952)
Fire Opal (Grace Mutell), 1899
Watercolor on rectangular ivory, 6 x 4¾ inches
Gift of Laura Coombs Hills
51.1926

NAME

ADDRESS

TELEPHONE

FACSIMILE

NAME

ADDRESS

TELEPHONE

FACSIMILE

NAME

ADDRESS

TELEPHONE

FACSIMILE

R

NAME

ADDRESS

TELEPHONE

FACSIMILE

NAME

ADDRESS

TELEPHONE

FACSIMILE

NAME

ADDRESS

TELEPHONE

FACSIMILE

NAME

ADDRESS

TELEPHONE

FACSIMILE

NAME

ADDRESS

TELEPHONE

FACSIMILE

NAME

ADDRESS

TELEPHONE

FACSIMILE

NAME

ADDRESS

TELEPHONE

FACSIMILE

NAME

ADDRESS

TELEPHONE

FACSIMILE

NAME

ADDRESS

TELEPHONE

FACSIMILE

NAME

ADDRESS

TELEPHONE

FACSIMILE

NAME

ADDRESS

TELEPHONE

FACSIMILE

NAME

ADDRESS

TELEPHONE

FACSIMILE

NAME

ADDRESS

TELEPHONE

FACSIMILE

NAME

ADDRESS

TELEPHONE

FACSIMILE

NAME

ADDRESS

TELEPHONE

FACSIMILE

NAME

ADDRESS

TELEPHONE

FACSIMILE

NAME

ADDRESS

TELEPHONE

FACSIMILE

R

NAME

ADDRESS

TELEPHONE

FACSIMILE

NAME

ADDRESS

TELEPHONE

FACSIMILE

NAME

ADDRESS

TELEPHONE

FACSIMILE

NAME

ADDRESS

TELEPHONE

FACSIMILE

NAME

ADDRESS

TELEPHONE

FACSIMILE

NAME

ADDRESS

TELEPHONE

FACSIMILE

NAME

ADDRESS

TELEPHONE

FACSIMILE

NAME

ADDRESS

TELEPHONE

FACSIMILE

NAME

ADDRESS

TELEPHONE

FACSIMILE

NAME

ADDRESS

TELEPHONE

FACSIMILE

NAME

ADDRESS

TELEPHONE

FACSIMILE

NAME

ADDRESS

TELEPHONE

FACSIMILE

R

NAME

ADDRESS

TELEPHONE

FACSIMILE

NAME

ADDRESS

TELEPHONE

FACSIMILE

NAME

ADDRESS

TELEPHONE

FACSIMILE

NAME

ADDRESS

TELEPHONE

FACSIMILE

NAME

ADDRESS

TELEPHONE

FACSIMILE

NAME

ADDRESS

TELEPHONE

FACSIMILE

S

Pierre Auguste Renoir
(French, 1841-1919)
Dance at Bougival, 1883 (detail)
Oil on canvas, 71⅝ x 38⅝ inches
Picture Fund

37.375

NAME

ADDRESS

TELEPHONE

FACSIMILE

NAME

ADDRESS

TELEPHONE

FACSIMILE

NAME

ADDRESS

TELEPHONE

FACSIMILE

NAME

ADDRESS

TELEPHONE

FACSIMILE

NAME

ADDRESS

TELEPHONE

FACSIMILE

NAME

ADDRESS

TELEPHONE

FACSIMILE

NAME

ADDRESS

TELEPHONE

FACSIMILE

NAME

ADDRESS

TELEPHONE

FACSIMILE

NAME

ADDRESS

TELEPHONE

FACSIMILE

S

NAME

ADDRESS

TELEPHONE

FACSIMILE

NAME

ADDRESS

TELEPHONE

FACSIMILE

NAME

ADDRESS

TELEPHONE

FACSIMILE

NAME

ADDRESS

TELEPHONE

FACSIMILE

NAME

ADDRESS

TELEPHONE

FACSIMILE

NAME

ADDRESS

TELEPHONE

FACSIMILE

NAME

ADDRESS

TELEPHONE

FACSIMILE

NAME

ADDRESS

TELEPHONE

FACSIMILE

NAME

ADDRESS

TELEPHONE

FACSIMILE

S

NAME

ADDRESS

TELEPHONE

FACSIMILE

NAME

ADDRESS

TELEPHONE

FACSIMILE

NAME

ADDRESS

TELEPHONE

FACSIMILE

NAME

ADDRESS

TELEPHONE

FACSIMILE

NAME

ADDRESS

TELEPHONE

FACSIMILE

NAME

ADDRESS

TELEPHONE

FACSIMILE

S

NAME

ADDRESS

TELEPHONE

FACSIMILE

NAME

ADDRESS

TELEPHONE

FACSIMILE

NAME

ADDRESS

TELEPHONE

FACSIMILE

NAME

ADDRESS

TELEPHONE

FACSIMILE

NAME

ADDRESS

TELEPHONE

FACSIMILE

NAME

ADDRESS

TELEPHONE

FACSIMILE

NAME

ADDRESS

TELEPHONE

FACSIMILE

NAME

ADDRESS

TELEPHONE

FACSIMILE

NAME

ADDRESS

TELEPHONE

FACSIMILE

NAME

ADDRESS

TELEPHONE

FACSIMILE

NAME

ADDRESS

TELEPHONE

FACSIMILE

NAME

ADDRESS

TELEPHONE

FACSIMILE

Henri de Toulouse Lautrec
(French, 1864-1901)
Mademoiselle Marcelle Lender,
Lithograph, printed in color,
13 x 9¾ inches
Bequest of Keith McLeod
52.1529

NAME

ADDRESS

TELEPHONE

FACSIMILE

NAME

ADDRESS

TELEPHONE

FACSIMILE

NAME

ADDRESS

TELEPHONE

FACSIMILE

NAME

ADDRESS

TELEPHONE

FACSIMILE

NAME

ADDRESS

TELEPHONE

FACSIMILE

NAME

ADDRESS

TELEPHONE

FACSIMILE

NAME

ADDRESS

TELEPHONE

FACSIMILE

NAME

ADDRESS

TELEPHONE

FACSIMILE

NAME

ADDRESS

TELEPHONE

FACSIMILE

T

NAME

ADDRESS

TELEPHONE

FACSIMILE

NAME

ADDRESS

TELEPHONE

FACSIMILE

NAME

ADDRESS

TELEPHONE

FACSIMILE

NAME

ADDRESS

TELEPHONE

FACSIMILE

NAME

ADDRESS

TELEPHONE

FACSIMILE

NAME

ADDRESS

TELEPHONE

FACSIMILE

T

NAME

ADDRESS

TELEPHONE

FACSIMILE

NAME

ADDRESS

TELEPHONE

FACSIMILE

NAME

ADDRESS

TELEPHONE

FACSIMILE

NAME

ADDRESS

TELEPHONE

FACSIMILE

NAME

ADDRESS

TELEPHONE

FACSIMILE

NAME

ADDRESS

TELEPHONE

FACSIMILE

NAME

ADDRESS

TELEPHONE

FACSIMILE

NAME

ADDRESS

TELEPHONE

FACSIMILE

NAME

ADDRESS

TELEPHONE

FACSIMILE

NAME

ADDRESS

TELEPHONE

FACSIMILE

NAME

ADDRESS

TELEPHONE

FACSIMILE

NAME

ADDRESS

TELEPHONE

FACSIMILE

T

NAME

ADDRESS

TELEPHONE

FACSIMILE

NAME

ADDRESS

TELEPHONE

FACSIMILE

NAME

ADDRESS

TELEPHONE

FACSIMILE

NAME

ADDRESS

TELEPHONE

FACSIMILE

NAME

ADDRESS

TELEPHONE

FACSIMILE

NAME

ADDRESS

TELEPHONE

FACSIMILE

NAME

ADDRESS

TELEPHONE

FACSIMILE

NAME

ADDRESS

TELEPHONE

FACSIMILE

NAME

ADDRESS

TELEPHONE

FACSIMILE

NAME

ADDRESS

TELEPHONE

FACSIMILE

NAME

ADDRESS

TELEPHONE

FACSIMILE

NAME

ADDRESS

TELEPHONE

FACSIMILE

U

Ernest L. Major
(American, 1863-1950)
Portrait of Miss F., about 1910
Oil on canvas, 40 x 30 inches
Gift of Harold and Esther Heins
1984.795

NAME

ADDRESS

TELEPHONE

FACSIMILE

NAME

ADDRESS

TELEPHONE

FACSIMILE

NAME

ADDRESS

TELEPHONE

FACSIMILE

NAME

ADDRESS

TELEPHONE

FACSIMILE

NAME

ADDRESS

TELEPHONE

FACSIMILE

NAME

ADDRESS

TELEPHONE

FACSIMILE

NAME

ADDRESS

TELEPHONE

FACSIMILE

NAME

ADDRESS

TELEPHONE

FACSIMILE

NAME

ADDRESS

TELEPHONE

FACSIMILE

U

NAME

ADDRESS

TELEPHONE

FACSIMILE

NAME

ADDRESS

TELEPHONE

FACSIMILE

NAME

ADDRESS

TELEPHONE

FACSIMILE

NAME

ADDRESS

TELEPHONE

FACSIMILE

NAME

ADDRESS

TELEPHONE

FACSIMILE

NAME

ADDRESS

TELEPHONE

FACSIMILE

NAME

ADDRESS

TELEPHONE

FACSIMILE

NAME

ADDRESS

TELEPHONE

FACSIMILE

NAME

ADDRESS

TELEPHONE

FACSIMILE

NAME

ADDRESS

TELEPHONE

FACSIMILE

U

NAME

ADDRESS

TELEPHONE

FACSIMILE

NAME

ADDRESS

TELEPHONE

FACSIMILE

NAME

ADDRESS

TELEPHONE

FACSIMILE

NAME

ADDRESS

TELEPHONE

FACSIMILE

NAME

ADDRESS

TELEPHONE

FACSIMILE

NAME

ADDRESS

TELEPHONE

FACSIMILE

NAME

ADDRESS

TELEPHONE

FACSIMILE

NAME

ADDRESS

TELEPHONE

FACSIMILE

NAME

ADDRESS

TELEPHONE

FACSIMILE

NAME

ADDRESS

TELEPHONE

FACSIMILE

NAME

ADDRESS

TELEPHONE

FACSIMILE

NAME

ADDRESS

TELEPHONE

FACSIMILE

NAME

ADDRESS

TELEPHONE

FACSIMILE

NAME

ADDRESS

TELEPHONE

FACSIMILE

NAME

ADDRESS

TELEPHONE

FACSIMILE

NAME

ADDRESS

TELEPHONE

FACSIMILE

NAME

ADDRESS

TELEPHONE

FACSIMILE

NAME

ADDRESS

TELEPHONE

FACSIMILE

V

Egon Scheile
(Austrian, 1890-1918)
Black crayon, watercolor, gouache, pencil
19 x 12½ inches
Edwin E. Jack Fund
65.1322

NAME

ADDRESS

TELEPHONE

FACSIMILE

NAME

ADDRESS

TELEPHONE

FACSIMILE

NAME

ADDRESS

TELEPHONE

FACSIMILE

NAME

ADDRESS

TELEPHONE

FACSIMILE

NAME

ADDRESS

TELEPHONE

FACSIMILE

NAME

ADDRESS

TELEPHONE

FACSIMILE

NAME

ADDRESS

TELEPHONE

FACSIMILE

NAME

ADDRESS

TELEPHONE

FACSIMILE

NAME

ADDRESS

TELEPHONE

FACSIMILE

V

NAME

ADDRESS

TELEPHONE

FACSIMILE

NAME

ADDRESS

TELEPHONE

FACSIMILE

NAME

ADDRESS

TELEPHONE

FACSIMILE

NAME

ADDRESS

TELEPHONE

FACSIMILE

NAME

ADDRESS

TELEPHONE

FACSIMILE

NAME

ADDRESS

TELEPHONE

FACSIMILE

NAME _____

ADDRESS _____
_____

TELEPHONE _____

FACSIMILE _____
_____

NAME _____

ADDRESS _____
_____

TELEPHONE _____

FACSIMILE _____
_____

NAME _____

ADDRESS _____
_____

TELEPHONE _____

FACSIMILE _____
_____

NAME _____

ADDRESS _____
_____

TELEPHONE _____

FACSIMILE _____
_____

NAME _____

ADDRESS _____
_____

TELEPHONE _____

FACSIMILE _____
_____

NAME _____

ADDRESS _____
_____

TELEPHONE _____

FACSIMILE _____
_____

NAME

ADDRESS

TELEPHONE

FACSIMILE

NAME

ADDRESS

TELEPHONE

FACSIMILE

NAME

ADDRESS

TELEPHONE

FACSIMILE

NAME

ADDRESS

TELEPHONE

FACSIMILE

NAME

ADDRESS

TELEPHONE

FACSIMILE

NAME

ADDRESS

TELEPHONE

FACSIMILE

William Morris Hunt
(American 1824-1879)
Frances Pickering Adams Winthrop, 1861
Oil on canvas, 47 x 36 inches
Gift through Miss Clara Bowdoin Winthrop
24.339

NAME

ADDRESS

TELEPHONE

FACSIMILE

NAME

ADDRESS

TELEPHONE

FACSIMILE

NAME

ADDRESS

TELEPHONE

FACSIMILE

NAME _____

ADDRESS _____

_____

TELEPHONE _____

FACSIMILE _____

_____

NAME _____

ADDRESS _____

_____

TELEPHONE _____

FACSIMILE _____

_____

NAME _____

ADDRESS _____

_____

TELEPHONE _____

FACSIMILE _____

_____

NAME _____

ADDRESS _____

_____

TELEPHONE _____

FACSIMILE _____

_____

NAME _____

ADDRESS _____

_____

TELEPHONE _____

FACSIMILE _____

_____

NAME _____

ADDRESS _____

_____

TELEPHONE _____

FACSIMILE _____

_____

W

NAME

ADDRESS

TELEPHONE

FACSIMILE

NAME

ADDRESS

TELEPHONE

FACSIMILE

NAME

ADDRESS

TELEPHONE

FACSIMILE

NAME

ADDRESS

TELEPHONE

FACSIMILE

NAME

ADDRESS

TELEPHONE

FACSIMILE

NAME

ADDRESS

TELEPHONE

FACSIMILE

NAME

ADDRESS

TELEPHONE

FACSIMILE

NAME

ADDRESS

TELEPHONE

FACSIMILE

NAME

ADDRESS

TELEPHONE

FACSIMILE

NAME

ADDRESS

TELEPHONE

FACSIMILE

NAME

ADDRESS

TELEPHONE

FACSIMILE

NAME

ADDRESS

TELEPHONE

FACSIMILE

NAME

ADDRESS

TELEPHONE

FACSIMILE

NAME

ADDRESS

TELEPHONE

FACSIMILE

NAME

ADDRESS

TELEPHONE

FACSIMILE

NAME

ADDRESS

TELEPHONE

FACSIMILE

W

NAME

ADDRESS

TELEPHONE

FACSIMILE

NAME

ADDRESS

TELEPHONE

FACSIMILE

NAME

ADDRESS

TELEPHONE

FACSIMILE

NAME

ADDRESS

TELEPHONE

FACSIMILE

NAME

ADDRESS

TELEPHONE

FACSIMILE

NAME

ADDRESS

TELEPHONE

FACSIMILE

W

NAME

ADDRESS

TELEPHONE

FACSIMILE

NAME

ADDRESS

TELEPHONE

FACSIMILE

NAME

ADDRESS

TELEPHONE

FACSIMILE

NAME

ADDRESS

TELEPHONE

FACSIMILE

NAME

ADDRESS

TELEPHONE

FACSIMILE

NAME

ADDRESS

TELEPHONE

FACSIMILE

Oscar Claude Monet
(French, 1840-1926)
*La Japonaise (Camille Monet in
Japanese Costume)*, 1876 (detail)
Oil on canvas, 91$\frac{1}{4}$ x 56 inches
1951 Purchase Fund
56.147

NAME

ADDRESS

TELEPHONE

FACSIMILE

NAME

ADDRESS

TELEPHONE

FACSIMILE

NAME

ADDRESS

TELEPHONE

FACSIMILE

NAME

ADDRESS

TELEPHONE

FACSIMILE

NAME

ADDRESS

TELEPHONE

FACSIMILE

NAME

ADDRESS

TELEPHONE

FACSIMILE

NAME

ADDRESS

TELEPHONE

FACSIMILE

NAME

ADDRESS

TELEPHONE

FACSIMILE

NAME

ADDRESS

TELEPHONE

FACSIMILE

NAME

ADDRESS

TELEPHONE

FACSIMILE

NAME

ADDRESS

TELEPHONE

FACSIMILE

NAME

ADDRESS

TELEPHONE

FACSIMILE

NAME

ADDRESS

TELEPHONE

FACSIMILE

NAME

ADDRESS

TELEPHONE

FACSIMILE

NAME

ADDRESS

TELEPHONE

FACSIMILE

NAME

ADDRESS

TELEPHONE

FACSIMILE

NAME

ADDRESS

TÉLEPHONE

FACSIMILE

NAME

ADDRESS

TELEPHONE

FACSIMILE

NAME

ADDRESS

TELEPHONE

FACSIMILE

NAME

ADDRESS

TELEPHONE

FACSIMILE

NAME

ADDRESS

TELEPHONE

FACSIMILE

NAME

ADDRESS

TELEPHONE

FACSIMILE

NAME

ADDRESS

TELEPHONE

FACSIMILE

NAME

ADDRESS

TELEPHONE

FACSIMILE

xY

NAME

ADDRESS

TELEPHONE

FACSIMILE

NAME

ADDRESS

TELEPHONE

FACSIMILE

NAME

ADDRESS

TELEPHONE

FACSIMILE

NAME

ADDRESS

TELEPHONE

FACSIMILE

NAME

ADDRESS

TELEPHONE

FACSIMILE

NAME

ADDRESS

TELEPHONE

FACSIMILE

NAME

ADDRESS

TELEPHONE

FACSIMILE

NAME

ADDRESS

TELEPHONE

FACSIMILE

NAME

ADDRESS

TELEPHONE

FACSIMILE

NAME

ADDRESS

TELEPHONE

FACSIMILE

NAME

ADDRESS

TELEPHONE

FACSIMILE

NAME

ADDRESS

TELEPHONE

FACSIMILE

Z

Z

Workshop of Botticelli (Alessandro Filipepi,
called Botticelli)
(Italian [Florentine], 1444/45-1510)
Virgin and Child with the Young Saint John the Baptist
Tempera on panel, 48¾ x 33¼ inches
Sarah Greene Timmins Fund

95.1372

NAME

ADDRESS

TELEPHONE

FACSIMILE

NAME

ADDRESS

TELEPHONE

FACSIMILE

NAME

ADDRESS

TELEPHONE

FACSIMILE

Z

NAME	NAME
ADDRESS	ADDRESS
TELEPHONE	TELEPHONE
FACSIMILE	FACSIMILE
NAME	NAME
ADDRESS	ADDRESS
TELEPHONE	TELEPHONE
FACSIMILE	FACSIMILE
NAME	NAME
ADDRESS	ADDRESS
TELEPHONE	TELEPHONE
FACSIMILE	FACSIMILE

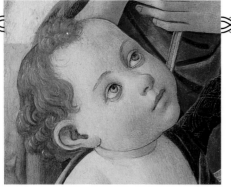

NAME

ADDRESS

TELEPHONE

FACSIMILE

NAME

ADDRESS

TELEPHONE

FACSIMILE

NAME

ADDRESS

TELEPHONE

FACSIMILE

NAME

ADDRESS

TELEPHONE

FACSIMILE

Z

NAME

ADDRESS

TELEPHONE

FACSIMILE

NAME

ADDRESS

TELEPHONE

FACSIMILE

NAME

ADDRESS

TELEPHONE

FACSIMILE

NAME

ADDRESS

TELEPHONE

FACSIMILE

NAME

ADDRESS

TELEPHONE

FACSIMILE

NAME

ADDRESS

TELEPHONE

FACSIMILE

Z

NAME

ADDRESS

TELEPHONE

FACSIMILE

NAME

ADDRESS

TELEPHONE

FACSIMILE

NAME

ADDRESS

TELEPHONE

FACSIMILE

NAME

ADDRESS

TELEPHONE

FACSIMILE

NAME

ADDRESS

TELEPHONE

FACSIMILE

NAME

ADDRESS

TELEPHONE

FACSIMILE

NAME

ADDRESS

TELEPHONE

FACSIMILE

NAME

ADDRESS

TELEPHONE

FACSIMILE

NAME

ADDRESS

TELEPHONE

FACSIMILE

NAME

ADDRESS

TELEPHONE

FACSIMILE

NAME

ADDRESS

TELEPHONE

FACSIMILE

NAME

ADDRESS

TELEPHONE

FACSIMILE